6

Six

Blue

Bus

Note for parents

The National Literacy Strategy includes a list of 45 'high frequency' words to be learnt by the end of Reception. You can find the list at the back of this book.

The simple sentences on each page have been composed of these essential high frequency words to give your child the practice and confidence they need to tackle their reading. The addition of stickers to find and place will help your child learn lots of words for things in the world around them, while becoming familiar with high frequency words in a fun way!

Start by reading this book to your child. When your child is familiar with all the new words, ask them to find the sticker words and pictures for each page.

As your child gains in confidence, encourage them to read the simple sentences and word labels by themselves.

TOP THAT™

I went to the park with my mum.

She makes me laugh and I love her.

Plane

House

Bike

I am going for a walk with my dad.

Can you see the cat?

He likes to go out at night.

Clock

I can count up to ten.

Can you count with me?

Yellow

Purple

Blue

Black

Green

I want to jump up and down in muddy puddles!

Rain

Shoe

Scarf

Coat

We like to play when it is sunny all day. Yesterday was sunny, too!

Kite

Bird

Knife

Cake

Bowl

Circle

Heart

Mum said 'Yes!',

when I asked her to play with me.

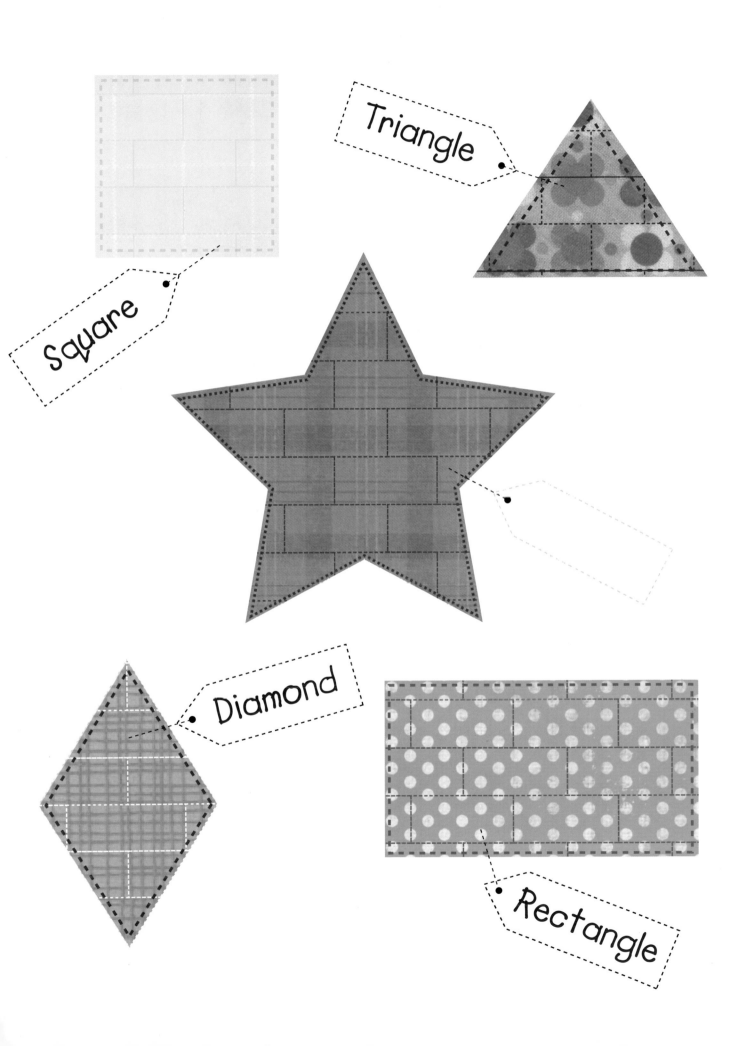

Triangle

Square

Diamond

Rectangle

'Come with me to get the shopping,'
said Dad.